Usborne English Readers

Level 2

The Snow Queen

Retold by Mairi Mackinnon

Illustrated by Elena Selivanova

English language consultant: Peter Viney

Contents

You can listen to the story online here:
www.usborneenglishreaders.com/
snowqueen

Little Gerda lived with her grandmother at the top of a tall house in the city. Their roof almost touched the roof of the house across the street. Gerda's best friend Kay lived there, and the two children often talked to each other through the open windows. In summer, they grew roses in the window boxes.

In winter they stayed warm, and listened
to Gerda's grandmother telling stories.

"Look at that snow!" said Grandmother.
"Somewhere out there in the middle of
the storm is the Snow Queen, my dears.
Every winter she comes down from her ice
palace, and flies all around the world in her
silver sleigh."

There was ice on the inside of the window. Kay put his warm hand on the glass until the ice melted. He looked out, and saw a lady's beautiful white face. She was wearing a silver crown, and her eyes were as bright and cold as stars. She was looking straight at him. Suddenly Kay felt a sharp pain in his eye, and another in his heart. He moved back from the window.

"Kay! What's the matter?" asked Gerda. She looked into his eye, but she couldn't see anything.

"Nothing. It's gone," said Kay – but he was wrong. He had a little piece of ice in his eye, and another in his heart.

Now everything he saw looked ugly, and every thought he had was unkind. He didn't want to play with Gerda, or listen to her grandmother. "Roses are for girls," he told them. "Stories are for babies." Instead, he went to play in the snow with the big boys in the town square.

One morning, he saw a silver sleigh in the square. There was a beautiful lady in it, and she was wearing a white fur coat and hat. She smiled at Kay. "Don't you remember me? Come and sit beside me."

She put her arm around him, and the sleigh started moving, faster and faster, through the town gate and up into the air. She gave Kay an ice-cold kiss, and he forgot all about Gerda and her grandmother.

Gerda didn't forget Kay, though. "What's happened to him?" she asked, but nobody knew. "Perhaps he fell in the river," said the big boys.

"Dear river," said Gerda, "do you have my friend? Will you take me to him?" She stepped into a little boat, and the river quickly carried her away from the city. Gerda was frightened at first, but she hoped to see Kay again soon.

At last the boat stopped near a little house. An old woman was sitting in the flower garden outside.

"Little girl, where have you come from?" asked the old woman.

Gerda explained about her friend. "Have you seen him?"

"I haven't," said the old woman, "but you are very tired. Come inside and rest." The old woman was a witch – not a bad one, but she was lonely. She started combing Gerda's golden hair, combing away all her thoughts of home.

"Sleep, my dear. Forget your friend. Stay with me." While Gerda was sleeping, the old woman went out to the garden. "Hide yourselves," she told the roses. "I want her to stay forever. I don't want her to remember her old life."

So Gerda stayed, and the old woman was kind to her. Gerda was happy enough, but sometimes she felt that there was something missing in her life. Then one morning, she saw the old woman's sun hat on a chair. It was made of cloth, with pictures of…

"Roses!" said Gerda. "There are no roses!"

Suddenly she remembered everything. She ran out of the house, and through the magic garden. Outside the garden, the spring and summer were over already, and there were no leaves on the trees. "Dear Kay, will I ever find you?"

Gerda walked and walked. She was cold and tired and hungry, and she sat down on a stone to rest.

"Good morning," said a black crow. "Where are you going, little girl?"

Gerda told the crow her story. "Have you seen him?" she asked. "Have you seen Kay?"

"Maybe I have," said the crow, "but I'm afraid he has forgotten you by now. He only thinks about the princess."

"The princess?" asked Gerda.

"The princess of our country. She is very beautiful and very wise, and one day she decided to look for a husband. So many princes and other rich gentlemen came to the palace! But when they met her, they couldn't think of anything to say, so she wasn't interested in them. Then a boy came. His clothes were poor, but he had nice clean hair and new boots –"

"That's Kay!" said Gerda. "I remember those boots!"

"Well, he talked to the princess in such a friendly way, and she liked him so much that now he is a prince."

"That's wonderful," said Gerda. "So how can I tell him that I'm here?"

"It's difficult," said the crow. "The princess's guards will send you away, I'm sure. Luckily I have a crow friend in the palace. I expect she can help. Wait here until this evening."

When it was dark, the crow came back with his friend, and they gave Gerda some bread from the palace kitchens. Gerda followed them through the gardens, and they showed her a little door. "This is the way to the princess's bedroom," said the crow's friend.

Gerda climbed the narrow stairs to a beautiful room. In it she saw two beds in the shape of flowers. In the white flower, the princess was sleeping. In the red flower there was a boy.

"Kay!" said Gerda happily, and the boy woke up… but it wasn't Kay.

Now the princess was awake, too. "Who are you? How did you get in here?"

Gerda told her story. "Oh, you poor child," said the princess. "Tonight you must sleep, but tomorrow we'll help you."

The next day, she gave Gerda some beautiful warm clothes, and a box full of cake and fruit for her journey. Then she showed Gerda a golden carriage with two white horses. "These are for you," she said. "I hope you find your friend soon."

"Oh, thank you!" said Gerda. She said goodbye to the prince and princess, and to the two crows, and left the palace.

She drove into a dark forest, and the carriage shone brightly between the tall trees. Some robbers saw it, and laughed. "A golden carriage, with no guards! We'll have that!" They jumped out from the trees, and caught the frightened horses.

An old robber woman with a long knife pulled Gerda out of the carriage. "Look at this one! I'll have her for my dinner."

Then a wild little girl with black hair bit the old woman. "Leave her alone! She can be my friend. Don't touch her, or I'll bite you again. We'll ride back to the castle in her carriage, and she can give me all her nice clothes."

"Are you a princess?" the robber girl asked Gerda.

"No," said Gerda, and she explained about Kay.

"Huh, don't worry about him," said the girl. "Wait until you see our castle. I'll show you all my animals."

The robbers' castle was big and dark, with an enormous fire burning in the hall.

There were some animal furs in one
corner, and they were the robber girl's bed.
Above the bed, there were a hundred wild
birds in wooden cages, and next to it there
was a reindeer, tied to the wall.

"This is Ba," said the girl. "He'd like to
run away from me, but he's frightened of
my knife." Gerda was frightened, too, but
she didn't say anything.

They had dinner by the enormous
fire, and then lay down on the furs.

"Tell me again about Kay," said the
robber girl.

"Kay, Kay is far away," sang the birds.

"Oh! Have you seen him?"
asked Gerda.

"We have, we have,"
sang the birds.
"He went away in
the Snow Queen's
sleigh. So cold,
so cold."

"Where were they going, do you know?"

"Probably to Lapland, where there is always ice and snow. Ask Ba."

"Yes, that's my country," said the reindeer. "It's a beautiful place. The Snow Queen has her summer palace there."

"I must find him! How can I get there?" asked Gerda.

"You should run away, tomorrow," said the robber girl, "when all the men are out and Mother is sleeping. Ba can carry you."

The next day, she gave Gerda some old clothes. "You can have your warm boots," she said. "You'll need them; but I'll keep your other things. Look, here's some bread and meat for you. Ba will take care of you. Now go!"

The reindeer ran and ran, out of the forest and over the snow. By day, the sun was weak and low in the sky. At night, the moon and stars were bright. "Look, this is my homeland," said Ba. "Now we'll need some more help."

They saw a little house in the snow. Its roof almost touched the ground. Inside, it was bright and warm, and an old woman was cooking fish. Gerda was so cold that she couldn't speak, so Ba told her story.

"My poor child, you must ride even further," said the old woman. "The Snow Queen is in her winter palace at the top of the world. She has Kay there with her. He thinks he is happy, but as long as he has those pieces of ice in his eye and in his heart, he can never escape."

"You're very wise," said Ba, "and I know you can do magic. Is there anything you can do to help Gerda?"

"She's stronger than she knows," said the old woman. "You'll see."

She gave Gerda some fish to eat, and helped her to get warm. Then she helped her again to climb on to Ba's back, and Gerda rode on towards the top of the world.

Then Ba stopped. "I can't go any further,"
he said. "You must walk out over the ice.
You're almost there." Now the snow was
all around Gerda, making the shapes of
enormous, snarling wild animals. These
were the Snow Queen's guards.

Gerda was terrified, and said a prayer.
Her prayer made angel-shapes in the cold
air. The angels fought the wild animals,
and Gerda was able to walk through
the gates and into the palace.

The walls of the palace were made of snow, and the doors and windows were made of icy wind. There were a hundred empty rooms, lit by the Northern Lights. In the middle was an enormous hall with a lake of ice, and in the middle of the lake was the Snow Queen's throne – but the Snow Queen wasn't there. She had gone to bring snowstorms to the warm countries of the south.

Beside the throne, Gerda saw a small, dark shape. It was a boy, playing with some pieces of ice. She ran to him and put her arms around him. "Kay! At last I've found you!" Her warm tears washed over Kay's face and body, and melted the little piece of ice in his heart.

"Gerda? Is it really you?" Now Kay was crying too, and his tears melted the piece of ice in his eye. "Where am I? What am I doing here? Oh, Gerda, it's so cold!"

Gerda took his hand. "Come with me.
Let's go home." Together they walked
out of the hall, through the snow palace and
across the ice. When they reached the land,
Ba was waiting to carry them to the old
woman's house. The old woman was happy
to see them, and gave them some more
warm clothes. Then they rode the reindeer
to the edge of the forest. There were new
green leaves on the trees already, and Gerda
saw someone that she knew well.

"Hello, Gerda! Hello, Ba!" The robber girl was riding a beautiful golden horse. "I'm going to see the world," she said. "So this is your friend Kay? Well, Kay, you're lucky that Gerda loves you so much, aren't you? I hope you love her too."

She said goodbye, and they rode on to the princess's palace. There were spring flowers in the palace gardens, but the princess and prince were not at home. "One day you'll meet them," Gerda told Kay. "They were very kind to me."

At last they reached the city, and climbed the stairs of Gerda's house. The sun was shining, Grandmother was sitting by the window, and they could see the roses outside. "Kay? Gerda?" she said. "Oh my dear children." She held them in her arms. They were all together again, and it was summer – warm, beautiful summer.

About Hans Christian Andersen

 Hans Christian Andersen was born in Denmark over 100 years ago. When he was just 14, he left home to become an actor. When it was hard to find acting work, he started writing.

Andersen loved to travel, and went to lots of European countries in his life. He wrote about the things he saw and the friends he made. His travel books were popular, but his most famous books are the stories he wrote for children, including *The Emperor's New Clothes*, *The Little Mermaid* and *The Ugly Duckling*.

The Snow Queen is Andersen's longest children's story, and one of his most popular stories today. Perhaps he got the idea for the Snow Queen's frozen palace from his travels to Sweden. And, like Gerda, Andersen loved listening to his grandmother's stories when he was a child.

Activities

The answers are on page 40.

Gerda and Kay

Choose the right sentence for each number.

A.

Come with me.
Let's go home.

B.

At last I've
found you!

C.

Nothing.
It's gone

D.

Gerda? Is it
really you?

E.

Kay! What's
the matter?

Mixed-up story

Can you put these pictures and sentences in order?

A.
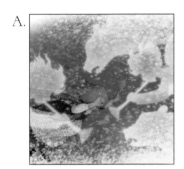

The angels fought the wild animals.

B.

Grandmother told Gerda and Kay stories.

C.

Ba carried Gerda all the way to Lapland.

D.

"Oh my dear children," said Grandmother.

E.

"Ba will take care of you," said the robber girl.

F.

Kay had ice in his heart and in his eye.

G.

The Snow Queen gave Kay an ice-cold kiss.

H.

Gerda arrived at the Snow Queen's Winter Palace.

I.

"Have you seen Kay?" Gerda asked the crow.

The Snow Queen

Which three things *can't* you see in the picture?

three white
horses

the Snow Queen

a golden
carriage

a silver
sleigh

houses in
the city

Gerda's
grandmother

the river

a fur coat
and hat

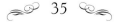

Beautiful roses

Choose the right sentence for each picture.

1.

A. They grew roses in the
window boxes.

B. They grew roses in
the garden.

2.

A. Gerda's hat had pictures
of roses.

B. The old woman's hat had
pictures of roses.

3.

A. There were roses on the
princess's golden carriage.

B. There were roses on the
princess's silver sleigh.

4.

A. There were roses
growing inside.

B. There were roses
growing outside.

How do they help?

Choose a word to finish each sentence.

1.

The crow has a friend in the ....

city forest palace

2.

The princess gives Gerda a .... coach.

cold golden magic

3.

The birds say that Kay is far ....

away north happier

4.

The robber girl gives Gerda some ....

furs food money

5.

Ba takes Gerda to ....

Scotland Finland Lapland

6.

The old woman helps Gerda to get ....

warm home shoes

Word list

able (adj) if you are able to do something, you can do it and nothing stops you.

angel (n) people believe that angels are good and powerful beings with wings, sent from God to help us.

bite, bit (v) to use your teeth to hurt someone.

cage (n) a box made of wood or metal bars, for keeping animals or birds so that they cannot run or fly away.

carriage (n) something that you ride in, usually pulled by horses.

comb (v) to make someone's hair neat and tidy, using a comb (which is like a hairbrush, but smaller and harder).

crow (n) a large black bird. Crows live in gardens and forests.

crown (n) a king or queen wears a crown on his or her head. It is usually made of gold and precious stones.

edge (n) the furthest or outside part of something.

fur (n) the short, soft, warm hair of an animal. Fur is sometimes used to make warm coats and hats.

gentleman (n) a polite word for a man, especially a man who is important but is not a king or a lord.

rose (n) a type of flower. People grow roses in gardens.

guard (n) a soldier who keeps a person or place safe.

hall (n) the first room in a house, or the biggest and grandest room in a palace or castle.

journey (n) when you travel, you go on a journey.

lady (n) a polite word for a woman, or a woman who is very important or grand.

lake (n) a large area of fresh water.

lit (adj) if something is lit, something else gives light to it or spreads light over it.

lonely (adj) when you are alone but
you don't want to be, you are lonely.

melt (v) when ice turns into water, it melts.

Northern Lights (n) a pattern of light, usually green and
purple, that you can see in the night sky in the far north.

pain (n) when something hurts you, you feel pain.

prayer (n) when you speak to God, or you
ask God to help you, you say a prayer.

reindeer (n) a kind of deer with thick,
warm fur that lives in the very far north.

robber (n) someone who steals things.

sharp (adj) if something is sharp,
it can cut you or hurt you.

sleigh (n) something like a carriage, usually
pulled by horses and used to travel across snow.

snarl (v) a dog or a wild animal
snarls to show that it is angry.

take care of (v) if you take care of someone,
you stay with them and make sure that
they are safe and comfortable.

tear (n) when you cry, the drops of water
that come from your eyes are tears.

terrified (adj) badly frightened.

throne (n) a special chair for a king or a queen.

tied (adj) if something is tied or tied up, it
has a string or rope around it and can't escape.

window box (n) a box below a window
for growing flowers and other plants.

wooden (adj) made of wood.

Answers

Gerda and Kay
1. E
2. C
3. D
4. B
5. A

Mixed-up story
B, F, G, I, E,
C, A, H, D

The Snow Queen
a golden carriage
Gerda's grandmother
the river

Beautiful roses
1. A
2. B
3. A
4. B

How do they help?
1. palace
2. golden
3. away
4. food
5. Lapland
6. warm

You can find information about other
Usborne English Readers here:
www.usborneenglishreaders.com

Designed by Jodie Smith
Series designer: Laura Nelson
Edited by Jane Chisholm
With thanks to Rosie Hore
Digital imaging: Nick Wakeford

Page 32: picture of Hans Christian Anderson © The Granger Collection/Topfoto

First published in 2017 by Usborne Publishing Ltd.,
Usborne House, 83-85 Saffron Hill, London EC1N 8RT, England.
www.usborne.com Copyright © 2017 Usborne Publishing Ltd.